Christino Lemmo

WHISPER
FROM THE
OCEAN

CHRISTINE LEMMON

PENMARK PUBLISHING, LLC

WHISPER FROM THE OCEAN

For information:
Penmark Publishing, LLC
www.penmarkpublishing.com

Cover art by Chris Tobias
Interior art © Paul Moore
Book Design by Windhaven Press, Auburn, NH

10 9 8 7 6 5 4 3 2 1

CONTENTS

Sanibel Scribbles

This book is dedicated to my grandmother,
Marge Tomaskovic,
And in loving memory of my grandfather,
Frank E. Tomaskovic (1926–2009)
Theirs was the most precious of loves,
binding them together as husband and wife for over sixty years!

My grandfather always told us grandchildren how proud he
was of us. If I could say anything to him, I'd tell him
I'm so proud of him, of the man he was!

AUTHOR'S NOTE

I'm often asked how I get ideas for my writing. In attempting to answer that, I laugh and switch the subject. Articulating it is hard, but I know exactly how I get my ideas.

While biking down Sanibel Island's Periwinkle Way with my husband and children, I had a burst of inspiration and ran into a store to ask for pen and paper. Unedited and exactly as I scribbled it on the scrap paper, that burst became one of the epigraphs in *Portion of the Sea*:

> *There are those times when a woman fears she is on the brink of extinction or that the dreams and wants she had for her life are endangered. It is then she must declare herself a refuge and take whatever measures to preserve her natural elements.*

When my boys were little, we were sitting near the shore and I was using coquina shells to teach my younger son his colors. As soon as one coquina would surface, my sons would have to shout its color before it shyly disappeared back into the sand. That night, I added to the first line of *Portion*:

> *I was shy, too, like those coquina shells.*

Watching a sunset at Blind Pass on Captiva Island, I asked my husband if he saw what I saw, that glistening pathway atop the water, as if you could get up from the sand and walk it. I couldn't stop thinking about the pathway the sun formed on the water. A few days later I learned that mother sea turtles lay their eggs, then follow the light of the moon on the water back out to sea, never to return to their eggs. At first, I struggled with how a mother of any kind could lay her eggs only to abandon them, until one day I learned that the mother sea turtles go out to sea in order to survive! I knew right away what I wanted to write, that no matter the circumstances, when life doesn't go her way and she's feeling down and depressed, there are always those "glistening steps" a woman must take for herself—steps that lead to survival—and it became a major theme in *Portion*.

One morning, while wading in the water at Sanibel's Light-house Beach, my older son went too deep and I made him come back closer to the shore. "Why?" he asked, and I told him there were things out there that could hurt him. "What?" he asked, and I told him sharks and things with teeth. "What else is under the water?" he asked and continued asking, and nothing I said satisfied him until I got home, and as all of us modern mothers do when our children ask us things we cannot answer, I went to the Internet and asked "Google" the question: What is found beneath the sea? My son was satisfied with the answer and once he and his brother were fast asleep, I relied on that research and wrote the part in *Portion* where Ava's heart drops into the water:

> . . . *disappearing beneath the surface, first struggling in*
> *that layer where the sun still penetrates, and soon, traveling*

down to the dimmer twilight zone, passing by strange and
bizarre fish and from there, entering the deep ocean layer
where no light goes . . .

And so on, thanks to the curiosity of my son.

I was writing one night I'll never forget, and I looked up from my computer, glanced out the window and spotted an owl on the branch of the banyan tree, looking directly in at me! The hair on my arms stood and, not wanting to move, not wanting to scare it away, I continued writing—writing him right into my scene, which became about wisdom, how Lydia wanted wisdom:

To me, Ava is a girl with the world's largest collection
of wisdom that she sought and chased after, gathered and
caught, as well as inherited, and I wondered how I might
go about finding some for myself—whether wisdom sits
perched on the branch of some special tree, or in the mind
of some older woman I might meet, I need a bit of it right
now, at this very age, and not when I am old.

During the writing of *Sand in My Eyes*, while pregnant, I would take a specific five-mile ride around the island on my "trike" daily, and continued this after my daughter was born, with her sitting on my lap. I would see a morning glory and, knowing very little about them, only that they often open for just one day and then die, I couldn't help but think that, like those morning glories, we don't know which day will be our last, so we may as well make each one spectacular, and I knew I had to write a silly little story about flowers and how the flowers all had something to say to us.

And the daisies, I always noticed them growing alongside trash cans and ugly parking lots, and thought, even in times of ugliness, there are always glimpses of beauty. If we look for it, we'll spot it (beauty in the world).

Ideas dropped easily as sea grape leaves from the trees—never forced—and often, on my walks or bike rides, by the time I hit Tarpon Bay Road on my way home, I didn't want more ideas because I'd have to keep them all inside me until after eight o'clock at night when the kids were asleep, and I could write.

There was a bird one day, crossing the road near Bailey's, and cars stopped. This particular day I was feeling down about my writing. A lady in the front car held her head out and, with a chuckle, said to me, "The birds have no fear!" After thinking about it my entire walk, I went home that night and, without fear, started to write. I even put a scene about a bird crossing the road, and moving forward with our life passions despite fear, into the story of *Sand in my Eyes.*

A lot of what went into *Sand in My Eyes* did come to me while in the midst of my mornings juggling three children, as well as the humdrum of life. I have notes scribbled on coloring pages, in crayon, on construction paper. I jotted ideas down on receipts—anything I could find to write on in the moment. I went through a phase where I liked to play Mozart every morning, and I would stand on my front porch with coffee in one hand and a baby on my hip, listening to Mozart and to the osprey in its nest outside my front door, thinking how important it is to live a beautiful life, to do little things, like play beautiful music and stand outside listening to the birds, and that I might not be as professionally productive as I once was, or thought I might be, but it didn't matter to me as much as living a beautiful life and having beautiful thoughts and a beautiful state of mind. In a roundabout way, I put all of that into my novel.

I could go on and on describing how I got ideas for this paragraph, or that sentence, or why in *Sand in my Eyes* I wrote one scene to take place at Ding Darling's Red Mangrove Overlook, but I won't. I will say that my ideas do *not* come to me because I live on a barrier island in the Gulf of Mexico. They do *not* come because I live a bike ride away from the beach and have the pleasure of watching sunsets frequently, or because I live in what people the world over call "paradise."

Ideas come to me because somewhere in my life, a long time ago, I learned how to listen to silent moments, how to be receptive. I learned how to cherish moments of contemplation, reflection and prayer, and realized that time spent alone with myself doesn't have to be boring or lonely; that within me—within all of us—are creative ideas as infinite as the waves of the whispering sea.

> *Sometimes ideas fall on me like little drops of water, but still, I pay attention to the small ideas, storing them away as if I had a pail on the beach for collecting things. Often, it's not until months after getting the ideas, when I am on my hands and knees in the sand, trying to build a castle, trying to write a novel, that I need those drops of water, and see at last how they are a part of the sea.*

Even when in the midst of chaos, or in the company of others, I have learned how to tap into my innermost depths. But always I start with prayer! For this reason, to me, inspiration is spiritual.

And usually, if my mind is clear and free of debris, it doesn't matter where I am, or what I am doing: changing a dirty diaper; making dinner for my family; carrying groceries up the stairs to my little house on stilts; or walking on the beach. I can do it! I can spot a creative moment as clearly as one spots a seashell, picks it up and, holding it to the ear, stops and listens. And that is my secret—I stop and listen. At first I always hear what sounds like just a whisper from the ocean. But then I hear more!

When asked how I get the ideas for my writing, that is what I really want to say to my readers. That is how I feel.

QUOTES FROM

PORTION OF
THE SEA

EXTINCTION (SURVIVAL)

There is a beginning, middle and end to every woman's life. But once a woman arrives at what she thinks might be her end, all she must do is reach deep down into her innermost depths and there she will find a new beginning. A woman is hardy as a perennial flower and deep as the sea.

There are those times when a woman fears she is on the brink of extinction or that the dreams and wants she had for her life are endangered. It is then that she must declare herself a refuge and take whatever measures to preserve her natural elements.

A strong woman knows what to do. She must pick up the paddles and with all her courage row out there, to her very own portion of the sea. She may have to row around in circles a bit, or dive down some, but soon she will spot them either bobbing in the water or resting on the floor of the sea, the treasures she thought she had lost for good.

Whether a heart full of love, or a soul that once prayed or a mind that loved learning, or the body that felt better, they are still her treasures and are waiting to be reclaimed.

So many steps a woman takes in her life will not be remembered. And most of her tracks will be erased. But there will always be those certain steps she'll never regret, the ones she'll never forget—those glistening steps she took for herself.

I think of the mother sea turtles and the steps they take in the darkness that lead them out to sea and I know there are steps we can take, too, no matter how dark life gets, steps that will lead us to survival.

Even in a mud puddle one might catch a glimpse of the moon glistening across the water.

Joy is an abundant and limitless natural resource within every woman and whenever it feels scarce, all she must do is tap into it.

It isn't fair to think that soon I'll be gone from the island like a living seashell yanked off the beach. It's as wrong as picking a sea oat and bothering a resting or nesting bird and littering on the beach and there should be laws against these sorts of things, and of taking a woman away from the one place she wants to be, the place she belongs. Life is brittle. It can be going along beautifully and all of a sudden a branch breaks and everything you are sitting on collapses to the ground.

There are certain circumstances, when put together all at the same time, that make a woman lose her mind, even those who haven't a history of mindlessness in their families.

It's okay for women to do that, to fall down from time to time.

I thought for a moment about all the impossibilities in the world. A manatee can't survive in cold water. A starfish can't move as fast as a shark. An osprey might look the part but can never turn into a bald eagle. And life can't always go the way we want.

It's sad when life becomes so busy that we touch our feet to the floor each morning, no longer noticing the birds singing outside our window. And birds sing everywhere—not just on some island.

TREASURES (DREAMS)

There is a time in every woman's life when pink is her favorite color, when anything is believable and the lines separating the possible and the impossible are blurred.

There are times when thinking hinders us from achieving the impossible.

There ought to be a refuge inside every woman where her joy can flutter and her wisdom breed and her dreams nest and her mistakes land softly and the words her mother or grandmother or others have spoken flap about like butterflies and all these things can mingle and thrive harmoniously as long as they like, or they can enter the world by way of her lips.

There are three treasures inside every woman: a heart, a mind and a soul. Each is priceless and worth far more than gold, silver, or diamonds. However, keeping these treasures locked up and hidden from the world will do her no good and bring her no pleasure.

Dig, dig deeper! Think hard about all that you want from your life. You've got to dig to find the real answers, to discover what you want. It's easy to live on the surface, so dig! Dig harder!

What is it about the reliable sunrise? A morning watching it paint the sky into a masterpiece brings my desires back to one thing: wanting beauty in my life.

I bent down and eyed the island's periwinkles. There were multitudes of them and they looked wild, ready to snap off and conquer the earth had they not been attached to their long, creeping, arching stems. They made me feel alive, strong and ready to do great things, but had me also wondering about the attachments holding me down.

The world is filled with cowardly dragons, people who chase after and tear down the dreams of others rather than chasing after and accomplishing their own.

A magical transformation occurs when someone tells you they believe in you. All of a sudden, you start believing in yourself. And soon, you start expecting and no longer need others believing in you because belief in yourself becomes enough.

Once a woman rides toward dreams and goals she never forgets how. She may fall down from time to time, but all she must do is to get back up. And when she does, she'll find she's stronger than she was before the fall.

ABUNDANT AS THE SEA (CHOICES)

There is a reason why women look back on their lives and regret the things they've done or haven't done. It's because they didn't notice the options and choices arriving on the shore until it was too late and those options and choices floated back out to sea. Rarely do the important options in life smack us in the face like a cold wave. Often those are the ones that come and go quietly with the tide and blend with our lives so that we didn't pay them attention.

As surely as I believe God created the sun and the moon and put the stars up in the sky and the granules of sand on the beaches, so do I believe we have natural resources placed within us as abundant as the sea, but if we don't believe and we don't tap into those resources, they'll lie dormant within us. And our lives will never change.

A woman's life follows a course as elaborate as the intricate interior kingdom of a seashell. At times she finds herself living, working, or spending her energy in a darkened area not to her liking, but soon she backs out of it or turns herself around and heads for another.

There are many corridors to explore and experience and a woman doesn't dwell her entire life in just one. But there will always be that one corridor that she remembers, the one with the glimpse of the sea, and it was the most beautiful of places to be, the one she'd return to if she could.

Sometimes people don't see they've got choices until it's too late and they wish they had done whatever it was they didn't do.

Just as a woman has the right to make her own choices, she also has the right to change her mind.

We all make our choices in life and we all have to live with the lives we created—until we make changes, that is.

A woman must accept the choices she's made and the ones she's left behind. And focus on where her tracks might go next.

ETERNAL BUTTERFLIES (SPIRITUALITY)

China breaks. A wedding dress dulls. Money gets spent. But the prayers a woman utters in her lifetime flutter back and forth throughout the generations like eternal butterflies landing ever-so-lightly on the shoulder of a daughter, granddaughter, great granddaughter, or any girl, often without her ever knowing.

I always assumed I'd save my prayer requests for a time when I might be starving, homeless or dying, but it dawned on me that two of those three things—starving and homeless—might never happen and the third—dying—would surely come but might come all of a sudden, leaving me no time for prayer, so I started praying right away and found comfort in it and realized why it was that people did it in the first place.

While rounding Sanibel's eastern end, I saw plovers, least terns and black skimmers nesting directly in the sand, which they do in the spring, and an ibis was flaunting its iridescent pink bill and legs.

I stopped walking and listened, and felt the Spirit of God hovering over me, subtle as those first signs of spring in Florida. Some say there aren't seasons in Florida, and others say God doesn't exit, but I've felt the seasons, and the spirit of God, and know they exist.

When living in the south, I start to miss the seasons up north, just as when I start getting too busy, I miss my God.

Some people have such a way of doing that—of believing in things they cannot see.

We're talking about faith. It's not like a pair of trousers you can hand down in the family. You can still hand it down, but it doesn't mean the next person is going to wear it.

Each generation is responsible for its salvation and that is not to say that the generation before doesn't have to do anything with regard to it. I do think a mother must equip and instruct and teach them everything leading up to it, then pray like crazy that her children will accept it. Praying for the souls of her children may be the most powerful gift a mother can give.

WHISPER FROM THE OCEAN
(WRITING)

The words a woman writes in her journal are like bits and pieces of her heart, soul and mind.

The first time I wrote in my journal, I felt like I was stepping into a world of vast lands, both unexplored and undeveloped, and along with it came responsibility to fill it up with beauty, and to leave only meaningful footprints behind, for starting my new journal was like being a pioneer arriving in a place of natural, primitive potential where I could cultivate whatever I wanted and I could hardly wait to plow through its pages.

I can't figure out if my desire to write comes from my mind or my soul.

Getting inspiration for writing a novel is like putting a seashell to your ear and listening. At first you think you hear what sounds like a whisper from the ocean, but then you hear more.

Reading and writing can change a girl's world. There's power in creating a world for your self.

Reading and writing about an interesting and adventurous fiction world is far better than living in a plain and boring real world.

FORMATION OF AN ISLAND
(BECOMING A WOMAN)

According to my mother, a girl is like an island in that she is constantly changing with time. And elements such as sunlight, wind and tides are constantly at work, altering her. When I asked her how a girl becomes a woman she said it's a process consisting of waves, gentle ripples, crashing surf and shifting sands. It's the coming together of small things over time that creates a woman.

Girls should be challenged to look ahead and ponder who it is they want to become and what sort of life they'd one day like for themselves. But people don't give it thought until they're grown up and disliking their lives and then they don't know what to do.

It's not important what we look like on the outside. It's all about our intellect and views on the inside. Besides, I don't care if there's dirt on my dress. It shows that I've got better things on my mind than striving to look like a prim and proper girl.

I knew I should take advantage of my looks before they left and I know most girls would find outer beauty a commodity, but I didn't want to be admired for my feathers or hunted down like those poor old Roseate Spoonbills. I wanted people to hear my whistle, to listen to what I had to say. I had a bold but honest whistle, the kind that hurts the ears of some and scares off others and only attracts a certain kind.

Girls trained to be perfect little ladies then enter the real world and don't know how to stand up for themselves or be rude to a rude person or strong in a bad situation.

I like a good debate. I don't know why people are so quick to end one before it ever starts.

Can a river otter stay away from water and an archeologist keep from an Indian mound and pelicans not go near Florida and the waves stop reaching the shore and a person spot a rare Junonia shell on the beach and pick up an olive shell instead? Can lovebugs separate? "Impossible," I said, "A girl can't stay away from the boy she loves!"

Stories aren't passed from one generation to the next with the intent of telling the younger ones what to do. But if the younger ones are at all wise, they'll pick up on a lesson or two here or there.

GLISTENING OBJECT (HEART)

I saw a gold object glistening like a treasure in the water behind the boat. It bobbed up and down for a moment, a beautiful piece of gold. And when it disappeared beneath the surface of the water I knew it was my heart.

I was leaving it behind. It was a solid heart and would surely sink. But first it would struggle as long as it could to remain just under the surface of the water, in that layer where the sun still penetrates, and soon it would travel down to the dimmer twilight zone, passing by strange and bizarre fish, and from there, maybe around midnight, it might turn a deeper red or even black as it entered the deep ocean layer where no light goes.

I don't know how long it might take for my heart to reach the pitch-black bottom layer, where the water is nearly freezing and its pressure immense. And it probably wouldn't stop there. My heart would continue downward to the forbidden trench at the very bottom and I could only hope that there it might dwell comfortably beside a starfish or a friendly tubeworm.

Despite such depths, my heart was strong and would go on

beating in that deep dark underworld. But I have no idea what happens to a woman when her heart sinks to that portion of the sea.

I couldn't release my love for him and it flourished deep within me, in that most precious of worlds, like the intricately woven interior of a seashell, the inside kingdom that every woman has, near her beating heart or its former site.

Soon I became like any other woman who simply thinks back fondly to the boy she once loved and wonders how his life turned out. Had he any hardships? True joy? A woman to love him? And most importantly, had he ever in the course of time thought of me in any way?

PICKING UP THE PADDLES
(MOTHERHOOD)

A mother knows how to travel that distance, risking mammoth waves and dangerous creatures in her path, but voyaging onward until she reaches the remote island of her daughter's innermost thoughts.

A woman loses an ounce of sanity with each child she has.

A mother does much that goes unnoticed until she is gone and then the cobwebs form and the dirt piles up and the house falls down.

A man can't feel what a woman feels when she's worried about her mama.

Little boys are meant to be outdoors, weather permitting. They're like puppy dogs. They need to be walked daily and a few times a day is better than just once and it doesn't matter that they were out the day before. They need to get out again!

Children want for their mommy's heart to beat wildly for their daddy.

It's hard being a mother. One moment I feel like I should announce that we are giving up ours lives in the city and staying on this island to be with the man I love, that a woman loving a man is more important than ambition. The next moment I wonder whether we should return to the city so I can teach her that nothing is more important than the ambitions a person has for their life. Then again, maybe I'm giving it too much thought and looking too deeply into it. Maybe a mother doesn't have such an impact on her daughter's life and it's no big deal what I choose to do. Maybe I should stay on this island with the man I love and teach her that there comes a time in life when a mother must do something for herself because if a mother sacrifices everything, including romantic love, for her children, they might grow up thinking that adult relationships aren't important, that nothing is as important as a woman pursuing her career.

There comes a time when a mother must pick up her paddles and row out there, to her very own portion of the sea, to reclaim the passions she tossed overboard when her children consumed her, the treasures she'd like to revisit now that they're grown.

It felt like yesterday when I was their age. Years are only big to young girls. To mothers years are nothing.

There is an age a woman reaches in which she starts to wonder about her own mother in terms of who she was as a person, heart, soul and mind. And she longs for a handed down treasure of sorts, or a story that might help put an intimate character description on her mother and what she loved and felt passionate about in life.

WASHING OVER US (SEASONS OF LIFE)

You know what maddens me most about winter? Winter stomps right over spring. And poor little spring hardly gets noticed anymore. And do you know what I loathe most about fall? Fall is winter's predecessor.

A gal knows she is in the winter of her life when family members nearly half her age start telling her what she should and shouldn't be doing.

Isn't that what happens to our lives? We look back and before we know it a new generation is washing over us. If they're fortunate, they might find a pair of our old shoes, and without knowing, walk in our tracks from time to time. But mostly, they'll make new ones of their own.

Those were the years when my children were young and I had no time to primp or powder my nose or care the least bit what I looked like, the times when there wasn't enough sunlight in the day to get done all that I had to do, the days when I'd walk into the kitchen and forget why I had gone in the first place, and the days when each of my four children had on average six requests per hour, so I ran around in circles like a turkey with its head cut off responding to and handling twenty-four requests per hour, making it an awfully long day, to the point of begging and pleading with the sun to go down, just so the kids would go to bed and all would be quiet and I could hear my own thoughts.

Those were the sleep-deprived days that put a few wrinkles around my eyes and the days that brought me as much joy as one gets from spending a playful afternoon at the beach and swimming and leaping over the waves and floating waist-high in that portion of the sea that is crowded with people and activity and lovely noise. If anyone asked, I'd have to say those were the days—my favorite portion of the sea!

QUOTES FROM

SAND IN MY EYES

FIERY FOREST (WORRIES)

It's what happens, when a woman pulls too heavy a load. up hills and down hills! Without fixing her weak spots. She tries making it further. She thinks she can, she can, she can. But then she stalls, then she breaks down.

Tucked within the blankets on my bed I learned that I can hide from the light of day, but haven't a clue how to hide from the contents of my mind—the worries and resentments that kept me up, returning in my sleep to the fiery forest where my smoldering thoughts had their way with me.

I had been operating for too long like a vehicle in perfect working condition, but there had been lights flashing in my head, strange noises in my mind, indicating a problem for months and cautioning me to slow down. But I didn't. I kept going.

A woman overwhelmed for too long becomes miserable.

I don't know why, but there are things in life no one will ever understand, things that are beyond our comprehension, defy logic and make no rational sense, like why did the cat run away with the spoon?

Such is life. Not everything can be blooming at once and sometimes it feels as if nothing is blooming at all.

If a woman lives in a cluttered mess for too long, her mind becomes like a junk drawer, with dusty thoughts and too much in it she doesn't need.

The first sip made my eyes tear, but the second went down smoothly. By my third sip I was drinking, not the way a mother is supposed to drink, but like a woman who has had a bad year. I was hoping the cognac with tropical orange might put things into perspective for me, like why being with this man made me feel the way I did—as if I were riding through the air on a very fine gander.

I took my seat on the bench and picked up my paddle, making a mental note to teach my daughter never to do the irrational things I've done, especially going out of her way, taking up activities she otherwise wouldn't, with the intention of bumping into a man. But hard as she tries, hard as she might, I said to myself, a woman can't always do the sensible thing.

Everyone I know is unhappy and I can't name a single person who is truly happy. And, to be honest, I think they are so comfortable being unhappy that happiness might be uncomfortable for them.

When faced with survival, life is no longer about passion and frolicking in self-thought as to who we are or who we might become. It's then that our survival mechanisms kick in, turning us into who we need to be.

I walked out my front door, got into my car and drove to Captiva Island, to the cemetery that lies next to the library, beside the Chapel by the Sea. There is no better place for a woman to go when she is grieving and missing horribly the person she used to be, back when life was simpler and more carefree.

A woman can go from room to room of her house trying to escape the noise and clutter, and then go outside that house to one of the most beautiful spots in the world, and the clutter and mess that's in her mind will find her.

A thirty-year-old grump turns into a fifty-year-old grump, and a fifty-year-old grump turns into an eighty-year-old grump. If I wasn't a grump at eighty, there's no way I'm going to become one at one hundred. Negative young wretches turn into negative old wretches if they don't do something to pull themselves out of their misery.

I've heard that as long as you crab to the Lord, it's called 'lamenting' and it's okay, productive. Whatever you want to call it, the daily woe-is-me complaining that I do, I've wasted too much precious time fooling my mind into believing I'm a prisoner in a dungeon, without pleasure and tortured, without freedom to change the things I dislike.

A woman stuck in a mangrove might look like a mangrove, taste like it, smell like it, but that doesn't make her a part of the mangrove. Once she gets herself out and washes off, she no longer looks, tastes, or feels like the mangrove, and it's the same with misery.

❧

THE HOUSE IS FALLING DOWN (MOTHERHOOD & FEELING OVERWHELMED)

As much as I love my children, more than anything in the world, motherhood and all my domestic responsibilities leave me little time for my own pursuits. It's a three-hundred-and-sixty-five-day-a-year job of nonstop reacting and responding, Monday through Sunday, from sunrise to sunset, as well as all through the night, without any break. Here I go again. I must sound like a blabbermouth.

It's hard being a mother, as hard as a woman climbing all four sides of Mount Everest every day all by herself, a solo expedition, with no time or energy left at the end of each day to celebrate her summits.

I'd like to focus more deeply on things that matter, but there are countless things demanding my attention and my energy daily—namely housework. It never gets done and, even after I spend a good four hours at it, five minutes after my children wake it's an embarrassing mess again. There's nothing I'd love more than to sit and read to them, or sing songs, or hold them in my arms all day long, but they have so many needs, crises and emergencies that, one-by-one, make up my day.

They never ask the simple stuff. It's always complex, like, "Mommy, why did my balloon pop, and the goldfish die and Daddy leave on a trip again? And why do the osprey return to the same nest year after year, and when will Daddy return?"

I remember the day I cried—felt for the first time like a full-fledged adult, all grown-up—no more youthful irresponsibility left in me. I was thirty-five and changing two dirty diapers, and also cleaning up vomit, while at the same time holding a teething, screaming baby on my hip. And I had the stomach flu! There was more going on, too, all at the same time, but it's a blur to me now.

What woman who isn't a mother herself doesn't want to pick up the phone and call her mother, tell her how overwhelming it all is, ask her how on earth can one fold so much laundry, and say, "Help! I'm going crazy. Help! I never knew it could be so hard," for there is no one better to call when the house is falling down.

Whether living up north, or down south, in a city or on an island, in a big house or a little house, clean house or messy house, loud house or quiet house, mornings for mothers are tough—especially mornings after having no sleep.

It's hard being a woman, harder a wife, but hardest of all is to be a mother.

When a woman isn't able to think during the day, her thoughts come out at night, darker and creepier.

A mother does things for her children, things that don't always make sense. A mother's love is illogical. It's a natural instinct kind of love.

Mornings couldn't care less whether a mother is rested or not.

My home was gruesome enough for a wildlife documentary and if there was a narrator, she'd have said, "This is a habitat in distress, in which a bird has been trying to create a nest out of chaos." But I was no bird in distress. I was an overwhelmed mother, wondering whether one too many crazy mornings mixed with lack of sleep might have a tragic cumulative effect, like one too many huffs and puffs and the house falls down.

No one told me it could be so hard, that motherhood would give me indescribable joy in exchange for who I was as an individual, and that the accumulation of it all, of worrying, caring for my children, responding to their every whimper, oh, and all the housework and grocery shopping, the cooking and cleaning, would turn me into this woman who has no time for waving, or smiling, or getting to know neighbors, and certainly no time for writing!

To an ordinary person, washing a pan is simple. But for a mother, who is also like a ringmaster in a three-ring circus, doing dishes is more hair-raisingly difficult than swallowing fire.

It's daunting sometimes, that my life and love belong first to my kids, and that at this stage in the game, the ages that they are, every waking hour, thought and action goes to them. But they're the brightest stars I see up there now, the reasons I look up when everything feels down. They're the only brilliancy I see to life lately.

Once a girl grows up and becomes a woman—especially a mother—there are incalculable balls she juggles, tricks she pulls, alterations she makes behind the curtains, and it all diminishes the wow effect of the magic, making it tough for her to stay awake and enjoy the show.

❧

UNDERGROUND ROOTS
(MOTHERHOOD & ITS SIGNIFICANCE)

I saw the marvel in my children's eyes, and knew then what a mother is supposed to do, show her children life in all its stages and that not everything is going to be blooming at once. Sometimes it feels as if nothing is blooming or will ever bloom again. A mother can only use words to tell her children so much. It's how she lives her life that teaches them the most.

What you are doing when your children are small is working on the underground roots, the things not seen, but vital below the earth.

What mother doesn't want to teach her children everything there is to know about life?

A rose is only as good as its last watering. It doesn't matter that it rained a month ago, or that a mother may have taken a half hour to herself a week ago. The roses need more rain now, and you mothers are only as good as your last beak.

All those menial tasks a mother does for her children will one day be significant, just as a pianist practices hours upon hours, years upon years, and no one hears all those times her fingers hit the keys. They only hear the concert. And the writer puts in untold hours of solitude at her computer—and no one sees all the work that goes into it as she types away before the rest of the world wakes, year after year. They only read the novel. No one in the world—but God—would know of my behind-the-scenes toiling over my children all the years of their lives thus far. They would only see the finished products, the masterpieces I was creating—the adults that I raise.

It's a woman's right to live and love, but those rights are altered when she must first consider the best interest of her children.

Mothering is hard. I don't know the secret to making it easier. You'll have to find amusement in the disorder of it all.

Every mother wants life to be better, more beautiful for her children than it was for her.

A mother's hug is like a flowering shrub that perfumes a room with a single branch.

A mother's fragrance can be noticed six feet away.

If a mother takes care of herself, she can give much of herself and no one will see what has been taken from her.

The roses should remind you to rest. One needs rest in order to bloom

again. I know it sounds hard, but mothers must take care of themselves. They more than anyone need sufficient rest.

No such thing as a woman with too many roses.

People always told me when my children were small—'Little kids, little
problems. Big kids, big problems.' It's true. Keep the temper tantrums
in perspective, because they grow up and you wish you were dealing
with a temper tantrum you could walk over.

Sometimes a mother does things that don't make sense at the time.
She does them for the well-being of her children.

Change—is okay. Be careful of planting yourself too deeply. Remain
flexible, moveable. The major cause of plant death after planting, by
the way, is planting too deep.

I fear I can't be the mother I wanted to be—one who gives her
daughter the lavish house, a cultural life in the city, ballet, voice and
piano lessons, and basically, the world. And as I go about without
passion, toiling under the sun, I worry that you're detecting it in
my eyes that your mother no longer knows who she is. When faced
with survival, life is no longer about passion and frolicking in self-
thought as to who we are or who we might become. It's then that
our survival mechanisms kick in, turning us into who we need to be.
And the Lord has stepped in, too, reminding me through it all who
I am—always with Him, and why I am here—to love the Lord, my
God with all my heart, soul and mind.

There is always that one type of flower, the one that everyone wants when it's in and seldom do nurseries have enough plants to supply its demand. It's the same with mothers—everyone wants them at once, and there's hardly enough to go around, to get everything done. That's okay. It's not always about being productive. Sometimes it's simply about being there. That's what everyone wants of a mother—for her to be there.

❦

STARS UP IN THE SKY
(PENDING DREAMS)

Sometimes a mother does that—she tosses her aspirations into the dirt and walks away, leaving them behind. It's not that she doesn't have the passion or desire to cultivate them, but that there are other things demanding her care and people who cannot flourish without her.

I remember how it felt when I was young, when there were as many options for me to choose from as there are stars up in the sky—infinite choices—with countless possibilities. And even after I married, I still believed I could become whoever it was in life I wanted to become. But then I became a mother—once, twice, three times—and don't get me wrong, I discovered for the first time in my life things like abundant joy and unconditional love, but when I looked up at the sky one night, I no longer saw any stars with my name on them. I don't wish all that many things in my life anymore, and most of the ones I do wish for are no longer about me.

It's a good thing, how all of a sudden a mother cares more about the choices her children will make in their lives than the ones she made in hers, and that if her own life doesn't measure up to her expectations—the dreams she set for herself—then it's okay as long as her children's lives are good.

I know they'll grow up and go off, and when they do, I want at that stage in my life to be more than a woman going for weekly pedicures—not that there's anything wrong with pedicures. I do like them, but I also want to be doing more, if you know what I mean. What exactly do I want, and who do I want to become? I don't know.

DANDELION IN MY HAND
(MOTHER'S LOVE FOR BABY)

I gave him a smile back that says, "don't mess with me," I'm a woman with three kids who hardly knows a shark from a dolphin, an osprey from an eagle, a roseate spoonbill from a flamingo, but I know everything there is to know about my three children, from their heads to their toes, and I know all there is about love, the unconditional kind that only a mother has.

I know, baby girl, that the day will come when you no longer see me for what I am, which is perfectly in love with you, and when you no longer want to sit in my arms or hear me sing, but expect more from me—That will be the day that I cry. But it's the other day I fear worse, the one I hear about from other mothers of daughters, the day in which you tell me you know everything and I know nothing. That will be the day I retreat into the corridors of my own insecurity, no longer daring to share with you all the things I felt were important. And so I will write it all down now, everything I want you to know about life, and when I'm gone someday and you reach that point—it usually happens to women once they have babies of their own—where you wonder whether your mother might have known a thing or two, you can pick up my writings and find out.

Babies don't stay babies forever, and you are to me now like a dandelion in my hand. With each breath I take you will change, lose your baby ways, and then I must let go of who you were. When that happens, I don't want to look back, perplexed that all of a sudden a big gust of wind came and took you away, and so I try now to be aware of the subtle breezes, the things I can't see with my eyes but can feel. And I'm trying to figure out how I can make it feel like forever that I am holding you—this dandelion—in my hand.

It doesn't matter how old a woman is, she will always miss her mother.

HIM AND THE BIRDS (FATHER)

There's so much I'd love to ask him today—things I wonder now at this age, but didn't think to ask back then, at that age. I'd do anything to have one more day with my dad—just me and him and the birds.

Dance to your daddy. It's what I wanted for myself when I was young, and what mothers want for their daughters, to love their fathers madly.

⟊⟋

MASTER GARDENERS
(MOTHERING GROWN CHILDREN)

B*ut what do I know? I'm just your mother. And all I can do is pray that my daughter, the one who used to wrap her arms around my neck and squeeze with all her might, the happy-go-lucky girl who talked a mile a minute and asked me questions as infinite and brilliant as the stars above, might reveal herself to me again.*

No mother wants to see her children hungry and coveting things they cannot have, but worse is when she sees them no longer dreaming, pursuing, seeing in their minds the things they believe in.

Like the walking iris, as children step out into the world, so does their mother. A mother stays attached to her children by way of her heart, soul and mind, as they go off, rooting lives of their own.

I was a counselor! All mothers are, whether they see it or not. We listen for years to our children's problems, starting in preschool when they come home telling us there's a bully hitting them over the head with a toy train. And it's then that we start giving advice, teaching them how to survive in the world, how to handle difficult people.

It's hard. It's an emotional transition at first, when children start doing what they're supposed to be doing, what we want them doing—living their own lives—they're like the seeds of a dandelion. All of a sudden they're separated from the parent plant and carried off by the wind, but don't worry. They'll be back. Trust me, one by one, they return.

Adult children love seeing that. They love seeing their parents out in the garden, doing what is necessary to keep their lives beautiful.

It's hard being the mother of small children, and harder the mother of teenagers, but the hardest of all is to be the mother of adult children who are no longer seeing the beauty in life.

When her children are grown, a mother can only do so much. She can no longer scold or punish them, cradle them in her arms or sing lullabies to them at bedtime. She hasn't the power to change her children's lives. All she can do is try not to judge, but pray and hope that she gave them when they were younger the tools needed to step out into their gardens and do their own work—to become master gardeners for their own lives!

There is nothing a mother longs to hear more than that her grown daughter is living a life she loves.

A mother has that right, to tweak reality, add a fictitious flair and get creative with the stories she passes on to her children. And an author has the right to declare fiction from fact.

When I think of pride, when I think about what mattered to me most, it was my children. They were the masterpieces I helped to create, the statues I sculpted, and the gardens I nurtured and grew.

What is a mother of grown children to do? She must look around at the garden she is in, which, by the way, is usually overgrown. Then she goes about creating a master plan for a new garden, something more suitable to her liking. And hopefully she puts her gardening gloves on, and gets down in that dirt and digs. She digs for the dreams she once had, the ones she buried.

MOUTH OF A SHARK (MARRIAGE)

When her children are away, a woman finds she still has her brain and all its functioning parts, and she is capable of loving, thinking, figuring things out, and of remembering all the expectations she had of marriage in the first place.

I craved for us, as a couple, to delve into the depths of the seen and unseen, sharing our reactions to the world, and getting to know better the spiritual forces that have the miraculous power to bind two people together for the duration of their existence on Earth. These were my original expectations, and what is wrong with being a high achiever when it comes to the person you are going to spend the duration of your physical life with?

I would never tell that my own children were at a higher point in the hierarchy of love than my husband, and for no other reason than that they were cuter and easier to love. For I had loved them from the moment I learned I was pregnant, whereas my husband, well, I didn't start liking him until the seventh date, and loving him until well after he proposed, and even then I questioned whether my love for him could last a lifetime. I'd throw myself into the mouth of a shark to save my children. I don't know whether I would do that for my husband, or not.

A woman, I told myself as I reached a wide-open area of Tarpon Bay, is allowed so many gray lies throughout her life. But then I stopped rowing, put my paddle down and leaned to the side, noticing in the reflection of the water how big my nose looked. It had to be an illusion. Water does that, distorts one's features. Still, I knew the truth, that my nose had grown. Not from all the white lies every woman tells, but from parading around like a cheerful soul, pretending my marriage was good and that the only love I needed was the mommy kind coming from my children, when in reality I longed for the romantic kind, too, the kind of love that lets a mommy feel like a woman. The truths a woman refuses to acknowledge about her life are the worst kind of lies.

VIEW OUT THE WINDOW (HOUSES)

Your house may be a dive but your soul is a mansion.

I like to believe that living in a small house with a good view out one's window is better than living in a mansion with no view at all.

Life doesn't always go the way we plan, and we either become resentful victims of our lives or we shift the way we view things in order to see the good. I've chosen the latter and no longer care so much about the house that I live in, but rather in what I see when I look out my window. Are there trees filled with red-bellied woodpeckers and nests full of ospreys? And when I leave through my front door, where does it lead? Should I go for a stroll, will I find nearby hideaways—nature's kingdoms?

What I care about now is, how many prayers do I have in my soul, ideas in my mind and memories in my heart? And, have I loved? Have I loved the Lord, my God, with all my heart, soul and mind, and have I loved another person abundantly and to the extreme?

Whether they loved me back or not, I do not care. But did I love extravagantly—for what a great sport it is—to love extravagantly in the sense of the action verb.

It's not how many rich people I have as my friends, or how much money I have in the bank, but do I know the words of Jesus, have I read the great literary masterpieces of our time, are the melodies of Mozart waltzing through my mind? Filling ourselves this way is important and goes into the makeup of a woman. When you're feeling underdressed and poor in worldly ways, you've got to ask yourself what you're made of. What are little girls who turn into women, made of?

WATCHING FOR WILDLIFE (WRITING)

E*veryone has their own story to write, sing or paint.*

Everyone has a story. Whether you build an empire from the ground up or raise a child, your lives are worthy books of their own.

There she was out my window, this older woman watering roses and loving her life, and the sight of it got me to thinking about the story I was writing. I no longer believed that a story about a young woman bemoaning her life was anything the world would want to read, nor was it the life I wanted to live.

I didn't want it to be an everyday, ordinary story, but rather, something life-altering, and I didn't care whether it would alter the lives of others. I only wanted it to alter my own, and it wasn't the story itself that I hoped might instigate change within me, but the process of writing it.

I was fully involved, in the creative zone, when one, two, buckle my shoe, three, four, there was a knock at my door.

Writing a novel, editing it slowly over time, revising it day after day is like chiseling away at tiny rocks. After a while all you see are the tiny rocks, not the fact that all those tiny rocks are part of the Grand Canyon.

Inspiration is real. It's like watching for wildlife. You need to be at a quiet, comfortable distance or you might disturb it. Sometimes it'll freeze and go away, but I try not to assertively approach it or force it. It shows up when it's ready, as long as it feels secure, as long as my mind is still and in a quiet, receptive state.

The thought of inspiration not existing produced within me a deep loneliness—the kind one might feel when alone in a house at night with nothing but the thoughts in their mind, because they don't believe in the soul.

I don't want the craving anymore, the craving to write. I'd be more carefree without it, without feeling compelled all the time to write. I don't mind feeling compelled. But every time I feel compelled to write, life gets in the way and there's something else I have to do, like change a dirty diaper, clean a messy house. I guess if I ignore it long enough— the craving to write—it'll go away.

And I will write! I will write to comfort me, write to counsel me, write to make sense of it all, and write to create for myself a better life, a life where dreams come true and people live happily ever after. Then again, it isn't as easy as it sounds when there is always someone or something getting in my way. It isn't the act of writing I find hard, but my finding an uninterrupted chunk of time in which to do it.

When I entered the wide-open bay I put the paddle down, letting the canoe slowly drift about under the morning sun while questioning how a mother knows when to give up certain selfish passions and fold laundry instead. I struggled with this, and needed to know whether I should hang my cravings to write out to dry until a different stage in life, or when I am old as Mrs. Aurelio and there is no one to answer to but the flowers in my yard.

A writer doesn't only pick her themes like apples from a tree; she prepares the ground, plants, grows, harvests, nurtures and processes those themes, too. It took a long time, and the process of writing it was hard, but I never wanted to look back one day and ask myself, *Why didn't I plant a Royal Poinciana?*

Writers are difficult people to know because writing will be their best friends.

Once a book is released into the world there is no going back, no changing the things you wish you could change, no spending more time with the chapters you knew you should have spent more time with. It's the same as when a loved one dies. There are no last kisses to be kissed, hugs to be hugged, words to be spoken—no going back, apologizing for what was or wasn't.

PLAYING IN THE DIRT (PASSIONS)

When alone, some people feel loneliness. Others feel inspired. And a girl walking through a field full of the Spirit, is never truly alone.

Ideas will remain ideas if you never pursue them. They'll be like seeds in a packet that never gets opened.

There are infinite things a woman must do in her lifetime, more things she doesn't want to do but has to do than there are things she wants to do and can. And whether she is doing what she wants to be doing or doing what she must, there is never sufficient time in a day to get it all done. All I can say is, cut out that which isn't needed in your garden, in your life, once or twice a year. Trim away that which serves no purpose and benefits neither you nor others. Trim it all away. And space your plants appropriately. Overplanting, crowding your days with too many commitments, activities and involvements, may lead to disease and fungus, and the things you want to do won't stand a chance of surviving.

When you pursue what you are passionate about, to others it might look like you are only playing in the dirt. But you will know the difference between playing and toiling in that toiling brings forth change in your life—even if that change is in your state of mind.

A wife and a mother sometimes feels a certain guilt when she plays frivolously, which is why sometimes she must keep quiet about what she is doing.

I'm sitting out here on a tree stump now—alone and inspired—overlooking my disturbed patch of soil and hoping I can do this right, grow roses not to eat, nor to wear, nor to live in, but to look at in and of themselves for no other reason than pure loveliness and delight.

⌑

PINCHING OFF SPENT BLOSSOMS (DISAPPOINTMENTS)

How should you be talking to yourself when you're feeling down and out? The same as you would to a flower when wanting it to bloom.

Self-doubts are like weeds, a constant part of life, but you must inhibit the weed seeds from germinating. I've learned to control them with the least amount of time and energy, but strong weeds, I've found, have a way of emerging through concrete.

When you try something over and over to the point of insanity and it still doesn't work, keep in mind that pinching off spent blossoms and leaves encourages other blossoms to open and makes their flowers last longer.

When you know with certainty that your leaves are spent, let go and move on. It's okay.

Holding onto your disappointments will result in loss of energy. Holding onto spent blossoms takes from the flower the energy it needs to stay alive. Trimming these away helps the flower to channel its energy to healthy parts.

Any time you put effort into something the world declares a failure, it only makes the future things you do more prolifically successful.

Women, like roses, need restful periods, too—non-productive times in their lives in order to prepare for their next bloom.

I took the sea grape leaves with me as I walked out the white picket gate of the cemetery, wanting never to forget that one day those leaves would be falling on me. The leaves inspired me, made me want to go home and do something spectacular with my time.

Every morning I watch the lilies grow and wonder, what am I doing to grow my own self?

A woman can build an empire—she can do anything she puts her mind to—in a distraction-free week to herself.

Not everything in our lives can be constantly blooming at once, and sometimes it appears as if nothing is blooming at all. You need to find some buds. There have got to be some buds!

When life gets ugly, look for the daisies! They're all over—in fields littered with trash, behind dumpsters, along highways. They might be mingling with the weeds, but you'll spot them if you look.

Everything in life takes a certain amount of work. If you think getting what you want in life is easy, then you may as well walk over to your neighbor's yard and steal one of her flowers when she isn't looking, because life isn't easy, nor is growing a garden, but once you start recognizing the pests and learning how to control the weeds, and all the other basics there are to learn, then the effort you put into your gardening becomes more pleasurable.

No matter how desolate life becomes, always search for beauty. Do whatever you must to find it. Do away with foolish clutter—in your house and in your mind—and you will find it. I promise.

Don't wait for a man to bring you flowers. Grow your own garden! Flowers don't have to be some untouchable luxury item that you get only once a year, on a birthday or anniversary. You should be out planting your own, surrounding yourself, creating for yourself a world of flowers. Especially when life is dull and its vibrancy fades, it is then you must go out and find your own fragrance. This is not as selfish as it sounds, for a single rose can be appreciated not only by your self, but by every pair of eyes that glances its way and every nose that stops to smell it.

Don't wait for any rose sale. A good rose is worth the price asked for it. But it's better to buy yourself a cheap rose, than no rose at all.

You are living, breathing masterpieces, created by God. Don't let the world trick you into thinking you are not beautiful, because you are, and true beauty never fades, never dulls.

Orchids are beautiful, but cannot change their variety, whereas a woman has the liberty to constantly adjust who she is, how she thinks, behaves, reacts, what she learns, pursues, talks about, as well as who she wants to be in life. And if she finds she no longer likes parts of herself, she has the ability to change what it is she no longer likes.

I don't care about conversations from yesterday, or feelings from the past. All I care about is what I'm currently planting in my garden, for what I plant today is what I will reap tomorrow.

Avoid unnecessary drama. Just as high winds are disturbing to roses because the flowers cannot easily stand being whipped about, the gusts and gales that go along with gossip and drama can damage you.

Don't for a minute think that, by pointing out the weeds in another's garden, it will make your garden look better. Au contraire! It'll only make your weeds stand out that much more.

Criticism has become a sport of the soul. Some hardy climbing roses resent pruning and will not bloom freely if they are rigorously pruned, whereas other varieties demand it. Choose your variety, and stay true.

There's no need for toxic chemicals. Keep your plants properly fertilized, mulched and watered, and you won't see many bugs. Set your boundaries, caring for and strengthening that which lies within, and you won't find many pests entering your space.

Life's sweetest moments do pop quickly, but I have to believe, that there are always more waiting to be had, for us to breathe life into.

DIRTY FEET (IMMERSING IN LIFE)

A person with dirty feet is a good thing. It shows she's real, a part of this world, and in touch with the earth.

I've always believed a woman should get down in the dirt on her hands and knees, and immerse herself into life.

A woman can't always explain her own actions other than by blaming natural laws for the way in which she conducts herself.

I wanted to believe that a person has choices in life, and that when one is lonely there are options, things they can do to pull themselves from the stagnant swamp.

It's your life! You can never take it too seriously. Most people don't take it seriously enough. They go about, never questioning discontentment. They live with it like it was the color of their eyes, something they can't change. Me? I can't do that. Call me a revolutionary, but if there's something I hate about my life, you better believe I'm going to set out to make radical changes.

Every so often a woman needs to step away from her life to see from afar how beautiful it is.

No one's garden is perfect all the time.

I hope you cultivate beauty in your mornings. Mornings are important. They set the mood for your entire day. It's why I start ours sitting out here listening to Mozart and the birds. Like classical music, nature has a strengthening effect. Listen to the birds and let them sing for you. It's good for the body and the soul in ways I do not understand, but know instinctively.

Some say life changes in the blink of an eye. Others say it changes with a mere thought. Chaos theorists claim the whole world changes with the single flap of a butterfly's wings, and that the ripple it sends out could spawn a hurricane. My life changed long ago, with a knock at my door, or rather, it changed with the opening of that door.

I've never met a person not looking for something.

Why do you have to know who you are? Why limit yourself?

The men of the house, they couldn't possibly understand my longing for beauty, the kind that flowers bring, and so I'm keeping it my secret, flipping through its pages, crying over the colorful pictures while wishing for flowers in our life.

No matter what your situation, never look at a rose as a luxury item. It is not. It is a necessity in a woman's life!

Despite these depressed times that seem to never end, we will look back on them as only a season of drought in our lives.

LIVING ON AN ISLAND (LONELINESS)

I was a lot of things back then, and a little bit of everything, especially lonely. It isn't only for old people. Even with three small children depending on her for their every whim, a woman can feel the loneliness that comes from not having another adult to talk with.

It doesn't matter where you live—a bustling city or a small-town island—a person can get lonely anywhere.

I realized it's a choice. Loneliness is a choice!

e ⁓

FADING HORIZONS (REGRETS)

I wish I hadn't gone on living miserably for so long—all that wasted time of my life. I do regret that.

There is no such thing as a wasted moment. Every moment of our lives holds significance. Even those we wish we could erase, the moments that made us cry, the ones in which we felt bored, or depressed, or angry. They all mean something, but only if we seek to find meaning in them. Search to discover meaning. Only then will you have no regrets.

Some friendships are like annuals that last no more than a season, but sure put on a good show. And there are the perennials, which are great, but you have to resign yourself to certain times of the years when they will be dormant.

It happens at a certain age. We question ourselves regarding the things we once did and said, and more so over the things we didn't do or say.

It's what too much time alone does to a person, makes them think of all the things they should have done and didn't, and makes them count the hours of their life, tallying up those that mattered, were truly worthwhile, versus those that were meaningless.

Time gone by makes it easy to forget the details surrounding why a woman once did what she did, said what she said, and reacted in the ways in which she reacted. It's why she's hard on herself looking back. But if she were thrown back in time, given a second chance, she'd do it all the same.

Should-haves, could-haves. I tossed mine in bags and tied them up years ago. Unless you feel like driving yourself into a state of depression, they're not worth a swarm of bees in May.

I didn't do everything the way I could have, but I did the best I could at that time. However, I was a worrywart, and I see now that most of my worrying was over nothing. Life happens whether you worry or not. It does no good, other than rob you of the moment. And I was busy all the time—overwhelmed. I look back and can hardly think of a time in my life when I wasn't busy with something. I wish I had spent more time doing nothing. Then again, look at me now. I have all the time in the world for doing nothing. So maybe I should have done more!

Regrets set in when all a person does is look back—when they're no longer moving forward. But this is life, right? And we are constantly moving from one phase to the next, redefining ourselves as we go.

I'll tell you I regret the things I didn't do in life more than the things I did. I wish I had pursued more of the ideas I had because I see it now—ideas not pursued are like seeds in a packet that never gets opened.

These are the thoughts that keep me up at night, if you want to know. When this whole place is sleeping and no volunteer visitors sit in that chair, I cling to the random memories of my life, wondering the same darn thing. Did I cultivate beauty each and every day?

My friend was like an overflowing fountain and needed to talk, to let it all out. I was thirsty and felt like listening, taking it all in. I wanted to hear more about the stages of life, especially the stage she was in now that I would be in, too, one day if I lived as long.

We store and collect, and all of a sudden the process reverses and we have to start shedding it all.

Some roses have one annual flowering that is astounding, while others have lovely clusters of blooms. And then there are those roses that do not bloom, but explode, only to drop their spent petals afterward. Such are the cycles of life.

I've watched the horizon fade before my eyes and I'm still here. The sun no longer illuminates the sky, but I'm still here.

Sometimes—on those days when no one comes by—what I wonder the most, is did my life matter?

When a rosebush isn't in bloom it still makes a lovely backdrop for those that are.

⌒

YELLOWING LEAVES (GROWING OLDER)

I had no idea then what being old was all about. It's just an extension of being young.

It happens when you're as old as me—people look at you like you're an exhibit in a museum. I just hope, if they stare at me long enough, something I say might make sense or sound wise so they can go home and feel satisfied.

The best time to move an established rose is when the rose is dormant.

There is always work to be done in one's garden, no matter the season, and we shouldn't let a frost line stop us.

I look in the mirror and wonder who the old woman is staring back at me. But I know that yellowing leaves are part of the normal aging process. Days like this, when I'm mourning the vibrant colors that *once were, I force myself to look up. And then I spot a cardinal sitting on a branch above me. I listen closely to its chirp. It sounds like this: "Pretty, chirp, chirp, chirp. Pretty, chirp, chirp, chirp."*

The birds sound lovely, but to tell you the truth, I miss those days when the parade came down my street, filling my yard with the sounds of bands and the clapping of hands, of children laughing and of babies not napping. Older women standing on the sidelines, watching us go by, used to yell out to me, "Those were the best years of my life! They go by fast! Enjoy," but I was too busy keeping children in line, marching this way, heading that way, mending costumes, tidying the streets, picking up confetti and candy wrappers, to think about my children marching on ahead of me one day.

But children grow up and yards become quiet. And it's sad when there are no reasons to roller skate, or floats to decorate, or candy to hand out, or little girls dancing about, and there is nowhere I can think of to march to, no routes to pursue, no band I can join or clap to.

I take my pen and paper and go down to the garden, where I sit like a flower stripped of her petals. How quickly it all happened, as though driven by a gust of wind—you were off and moved away. It's hard going about my days with the most precious part of me—you, my daughter—off and into the world, and I see now why it is wise for a woman to have a few things going on in her life so that when petals blow off she still has other things surrounding her.

THROUGH WINTER AND THROUGH SPRING (FAITH)

On those mornings when I awake and feel overwhelmed, defeated, exhausted with regard to what has become my life, when all I want to do is turn over in bed and crawl under my pillow to hide, I force myself to open this book of roses, to look at the colorful pictures. I read from the Bible, too, and then pray, begging that the dull and boring routine which is my life will blossom into more. After doing this, I find my mind unfurling and I see my dreams and work on them in my mind. I've done this so many times that my dreams have become far greater than I originally imagined, and it's because I'm seeing instead the dreams that the Lord has for my life. The creator of the shells on the shore and the fish in the sea has adjusted my small way of thinking to dreaming bigger for my life.

I will not cry when the hummingbirds are gone because I feel all the time the spirit of the Lord hovering above me, and there is no greater thing on Earth—no breeze coming from the north, south, east or west, or raindrops from above—than experiencing that, than feeling the hair on your arms standing because you know, not because you've seen, or touched or heard about it from someone else, but because you know firsthand that it is true, that the good Lord does exist and that he is here and there and everywhere, through winter and through spring.

Each morning glory unfurls only once, has one life to live, then it closes and dies. It didn't take me long to know what the spirit of God was trying to tell me through the flowers, that like the morning glories I had one life to live, and this is my life!

Orchids ought to remind us women how strong and resilient we are, more so than the world believed.

Delight in your days. It's your life! Make it a life you relish! A life you are proud of! Live—live your life!

One moment you're sitting around admiring a bouquet of flowers on your kitchen table, and the next they have wilted, with their petals fallen to the floor. Houses burn and automobiles break down, jewels get stolen, babies grow old and loved ones disappoint. Everything in life will dry up and crumble to the ground, but a soul in love with the Lord remains intact for eternity.

I pray that you will spot the wildflowers hidden within the weeds. Look for the wild petunias and think of them. They bloom for one morning or day, and then die. We don't know the number of our days so, like the wild petunia, why not make each current day we do have spectacular?

I know nothing I say or do is going to prevent or protect my children from the infinite problems of life, which like waves from the ocean keep coming at you one mammoth challenge after the next. No sooner do you deal with one than you are hit by another, until one day you find yourself no longer seeing the beauty of it all. It's as if you're walking around with sand in your eyes.

Here I go unfurling my most intimate wish for you, that when life has you no longer seeing beauty or believing in good, that you cry out to the Lord. He is the only one, I have found, who can wash my eyes clean. And because problems are a part of living, as infinite as the grains of sand on the seashore, I find myself crying out to Him almost every day.

Because not everything will be blooming all the time, it is my prayer for you that each and every morning of your life, and in every season, you wake to birds singing out your window. And when there are no birds, or window, that you wake up singing yourself, and when you have nothing good to sing, that your soul will sing for you, to remind you in some roundabout way that this is the day that the Lord hath made and only He can turn your bad days good, making you feel as if you're flying above those waves on the wings of a Great White Heron.

DOLPHIN IN THE BAY
(DEAR CHILDREN)

You are like the cardinal in the tree that makes me smile,
No, you mean more to me than the cardinal in the tree that makes
  me smile.
You are the child who makes me sing.
You are like a ruby-throated hummingbird that makes me smile.
No, you mean more to me than a ruby-throated hummingbird that
  makes me smile.
You are the child who makes my thoughts flutter.
You are like the dolphin in the bay that makes me smile.
No, you mean more to me than the dolphin in the bay that makes
  me smile.
You are the child who makes my heart leap.
You are like a treasure on the island that makes me smile.
No, you mean more to me than a treasure on an island that makes
  me smile.
You are the child who makes my eyes glisten.
You are the manatee in the canal that makes me smile.
No, you mean more to me than the manatee in the canal that makes
  me smile.

You are the child who makes me cherish each moment and move slower through life.

DEAR CHILD:
When I look out my window I see an osprey soaring through the sky,
But when I look at you I see you doing more.
When I pull you in the wagon we see a turtle diligently digging a hole,
But when I look at you I see you doing more.
When I take you to the shore I see a big boy building castles out of sand,
But when I look at you I see you doing more.
When I take you for a ride at night, I see the lighthouse lighting up the Gulf so bright,
But when I look at you I see you doing more.
When I push you on the swing, we see the trees reaching up to Heaven,
But when I look at you I see you doing more.
When I look at you, my son, I see the things that you can be,
And I also see bits of me.
I see all the things I wanted to be, the things I wanted to do,
But then I see more.

DEAR CHILD.
I've never been into bird-watching until I had you,
And now I spend my life doing nothing but watching you.
To me you're like a little bird,
The kind through our windows you've heard,
A newly hatched osprey wanting to fly,
A screeching owl demanding "why"

A growing pelican I struggle to keep fed,
And a noisy woodpecker that wakes me from bed.

I've never been into collecting shells until I had you,
And now I spend my life collecting things for you.
To me you're one of those rare and unique shells,
The kind one finds along the shore, then likes to show and tell,
A rare junonia I will cherish forever,
A jingle shell attached to my hip wherever,
A conch shell I hold to my ear as you importantly blab,
And sorry, darling, but sometimes you're simply a crab!

I've never had time for smelling flowers until I had you,
And now I spend my life smelling them with you.
To me you're every bit as beautiful as the flowers,
The kind I could look at and hold for hours.
A morning glory that wakes me each day,
A rose that reminds me to rest, then play,
A periwinkle that keeps my priorities real,
And an orchid that cares about how I feel.

I've never had, but always wanted a parrot of my own,
And now I spend my life teaching you how to talk.
To me you were already a beauty before you had feathers,
The kind I want to fly with through good and bad weather.
A bird I can nurture in my nest for awhile,
A bird I can train using my own innate style.
A bird that will one day leave my nest and say good-bye,
And then return to tell me of her soaring through the sky.

QUOTES FROM

SANIBEL SCRIBBLES

MARKING THEIR WINGS (GRIEF)

How dare winter arrive in the season of spring? How dare it show up cruelly, catching everyone off guard? How dare a tulip wither before its time?

I got so upset that time I visited Grandma on Sanibel, and it rained every day. Now I'd give anything for a rain-spent day inside with my grandmother. No, we cannot control rain or death.

I felt like a hypocrite. How dare a believer in God fear death?

In college, I took classes on everything from world religions to ancient philosophy to chemistry to biology, but everything focused on life. Not death. So how dare a believer in God fear death? Well, it was a great question because I did.

The realization that I'm not going to live on this earth forever, that my life here is not permanent, shocked me. I've never thought about death before.

One can determine the life span of butterflies by capturing them and marking their wings with a square-tipped marking pen, then watching for them later. I don't want to be captured. I don't want to know the number of my days.

Everybody will lose someone or something they love at some point in this life, as we know it. Losses great and small come in various ways. Some people will grieve; others will be grief-stricken. I recommend actively grieving, I mean going on a grief journey. Grieving is a long process. You have to rediscover the world about you.

Some will turn their grievances into fears and phobias. Others will turn their grievances into an appreciation for life, for the living moment itself, the present.

The cup-shaped, solitary flowers died each year, but every winter their bulbs divided under the snow-packed earth, and new ones bloomed in the spring.

Remember the tulips. Just as their season of stardom comes and goes, you too will one day pass.

We're all dying. Your mother, your father, your siblings if you have any, your friends, every one of us on this island, on this planet, we're all dying. Some people are already dead, and others have never lived at all. We were born to die, and every single day of life means one less day of our life.

Wouldn't this be a better world if children grew up aware of the fact that this life is quite short?

TIME, WEATHER AND DEATH—these three words transcend any culture and language. These three things are completely out of our control, yet everything is planned around them. Even if a fiesta is planned for manana, TIME moves on at its own pace, turning that fiesta into nothing more than a memory. WEATHER behaves rudely, when it likes, pouring rain on the guests of the fiesta. DEATH, should it be told, shows up just before the fiesta. And for that person, who may have been living in a countdown of anticipation, the fiesta never comes. This is why people fear death. They cannot control it.

The tulips my friend and I had seen together last spring had disappeared, their season of stardom past. As surely as the seasons would come and go, new tulips would return to take their place in the same soil come early May.

I'll never forget my dark days of not knowing how to grieve, or handle death, or deal with loss or change or new things to come, whatever they might be

⌒⌒

CONFIDENT VESSELS (WORRYING)

*I*f rain took into consideration all the events it might ruin on any given day or night, the world might shrivel up into dryness because rain worried so much.

I want to face uncertainty in life like a confident vessel moving forward through dark waters. I also want to know when storms are coming my way so I don't get hit. How can I turn around or take another route in time if I don't know storms are approaching?

Everyone has fears in life. Some fear the future. Some fear not measuring up to what this world declares a success. Some fear not making their dreams and goals come true by an exact age at which they fantasized them to be a reality. Some fear not having a fortune in the bank by the age of thirty or not owning a house by thirty-five.

Much happens between the hours of sunset and sunrise. Sometimes, issues become clear in late-night conversations or spells of insomnia or prayers. Other times, they work themselves out in our dreams, as our brains surrender to another existence, and in the morning, our subconscious minds have it all figured out for us.

I feel alone, but know we are not alone for a single moment. We are surrounded by beings we cannot see. How I would love to put on glasses that allow me to see their mammoth white wings glistening and surrounding me like bodyguards!

Masking one problem with another could lead to self-destruction.

SWITCHING SHELLS (COMFORT ZONES)

Leaving a hometown is like burning the fingerprints right off one's hand. Arriving in a new town, someone else's hometown, is like asking to borrow someone else's prints.

I worry about the geographic scattering of the American family and the evaporation of hometowns. If only I could become a hermit crab, carrying my home with me, switching shells only as I grow and need to switch shells.

Sometimes I need to mentally pamper myself for existing in a constantly changing world. There is no harm in pampering one's soul from time to time, acknowledging its journey.

The very thought of leaving a comfort zone makes me feel queasy, as if there are newly hatching caterpillars in my gut and they're nibbling on their eggshells.

I love coffee shops. To me, they're therapeutic refuges from the world, philosophical havens and retreats for modern-day mourning.

I understand why woodpeckers carve out holes in tree trunks, leave, and then return to the same hole year after year. There is something about the concept of going home that sounds right.

Tulips make me want to dance and scrub streets with buckets of cold water and old-fashioned brooms. Tulips mark every corner of my hometown, and make me homesick, too.

I shop and shop for shoes but no one sells the wooden kind and it's sad because wooden shoes remind me of whom I am and where I came from.

THROUGH CHOPPY WATERS
(LIFE'S JOURNEYS)

We're all like ships, coming and going, anchoring for a moment and gone the next. And we're all propelled through life by different things. Some make their way by oar and sails, and others by paddles and poles. Some have steam engines and boilers, and some internal-combustion engines or outboard motors. Some go through life in a purely recreational manner, while others stay practical. If a vessel is determined enough to stay on course, it will be strong enough to resist the waves banging against it. Some of us take on water and sink from time to time, while others constantly work to stay afloat. I've met all these vessels.

The canals we go down might not make sense as we're cruising along, but there's a reason why our motors run out of fuel, get caught up in a mangrove or run aground from time to time. Everyone needs to discover an island where they can stop and think: to think magnificent thoughts they have never had time to ponder before and to notice magnificent details they have never noticed before.

You do need to figure out how you want to reach each spot, what kind of fuel you want to use and what sorts of repairs you might need along the way. Anchor long enough to repair and refuel but always work your way through dark waters.

It's amazing how a lady gives birth to two babies. One grows up to be a destroyer, advancing to a makeshift raft, and the other is a caravel, who travels the world accumulating gold and silver. I don't know why we take such different routes. I only know our mothers give us the basic materials and send us off into the waters of this world. It's up to us to create the sort of vessels we wanted to be.

You say you have never been on a journey? You have never been unemployed, unable to land a job? You have never said good-bye to someone you love? You have never lost something precious? You have never feared anything in life? You have never felt under the weather or like you were drowning? Don't underestimate the journeys you've been on. They don't have to be geographical or physical journeys. Everyone has their dark days of life when the storms feel never-ending. Often these journeys make up the women that you are and the ones you are becoming.

Why can't I be sad? What, don't worry-be happy? Listen, if something happens in life, and you feel sad, I'm not going to tell you to rent a funny movie. You know why? That movie's going to end and you're going to feel sad again. No, let yourself feel down. It's okay to feel down. I'm sick and tired of this world not letting people feel down. The theme of our world is be happy, but I think we all need to have days, weeks and sometimes months of feeling sad. I think it's part of life, that's what I think. We're going to go through dark water, and sometimes we can't make it out in one day, it's too big.

It doesn't matter where you come from, or where you are going. The waters of the lakes can be as unpredictable as the waters of the sea, and both have caused many shipwrecks.

As a submarine that has traveled from Lake Michigan to the Gulf of Mexico, to the Mediterranean Sea, and Pacific Ocean, I never want to forget the route I have traveled, and look forward to the route ahead.

When I am old, I hope I look seasoned, like a woman who has sailed through life, through choppy water, through calm water, through storms and through sunsets.

There's so much I once wanted to do in life, and now I just want to savor life. Have I lost my ambition? No, I don't believe so.

AN ISLAND OF YOUR OWN
(STOPPING TO THINK)

Discover an island where you can rediscover yourself.

Often we keep ourselves so busy that we never allow ourselves to think. Running around from dot-to-dot on our never-ending list of things-to-do only keeps us from the things we don't want to think about. That is why we must discover islands of our own.

There are islands everywhere waiting to be discovered. Everyone needs to find an island where they can stop and think, relearn who they are in relation to the ever-evolving world. Some hardly need to venture at all, but others will find themselves voyaging out, not necessarily to a real island like Sanibel or Captiva, but something more remote— their own lost continent of Atlantis, a place of revitalization.

I've made my choice. I'm leaving for an island in the morning. And that's all I'm going to say about that.

A woman living on an island sometimes feels a need to leave for an even farther island. She needs more space, more solitude, and more time away from things.

Everywhere I live I eventually discover a place to think, to dwell, to escape. The world is large and easily overwhelming, and that is why it must be broken down. That is why people of all ages need to find their little hiding places in life, even if it's a closet in your house. That closet in your house, which is in a state, which is in a country, which is in a continent, which lies in an ocean, which is in the world, which is a spec in the galaxy, becomes your very own secret destination and is like traveling to infinity in your mind without leaving your comfort zone.

Who has time for thinking? I don't, so I make time.

I haven't a real garden. But I've created a place I can go to in my mind.

A tulip needs morning sun to open. As much as that tulip needs morning sun, a woman needs time alone. She discovers immense power from within, power she never knew she had, once she spends a moment with herself.

I long for quiet moments as much as a woman on a trapeze, when trying to balance requires it, aware that the very next noise might distract her or throw her off course, sending her and the thoughts she needed into midair, then crashing to the ground.

I feel lonely, and all I have are my own annoying thoughts to keep me company.

I want to enjoy my own company. Why shouldn't I? I have to live with it the rest of my life. And still, after death, I have to live with my mind, my soul, my spirit, myself.

SYMPHONY
(CHERISHING SILENT MOMENTS)

There are four parts to a symphony. There is silence between each of the parts. How dare anyone clap during a moment meant for silence?

Do as you like with your moments of silence.

Some people don't know what to do in the silence. They don't know how to feel and so they fill it up with noise. I don't even like whispering during the silent moments. I just want to listen.

I listen to the symphony and let the music surround my body like a powerful electromagnetic field. I feel stronger and healthier, as if the music adds strength to my immune system.

You say you have never gone to a symphony, but you have and you did not just sit there. You were the conductor! A person conducts countless symphonies in their life. And what does the conductor do? She sets the volume and the speed, and interprets the music the composer has written.

Every symphony has four parts, four movements of music. Between those four movements, there is silence. It is up to you to do as you like in your moments of silence.

Sometimes I can hardly contain myself, like a woman sitting quietly through an entire symphony, bottling her desire to clap and scream and shout within herself like a bottle of champagne and now ready to explode with excitement, I could jump up and do an angel in the snow if only there was snow.

Even on this subtropical island, I do an angel in the sand and with my eyes closed, I am wherever I want to be and can feel the refreshing coldness of Michigan's wintry mantle.

How will you know when one symphony has ended? Believe me, you'll know!

There will surely be other symphonies in my life, but this particular one I declare done. I will always hear the memory of its music in my mind, and now, in the immediate silence following that music, I value my time and the very moment.

I understand now that silence serves a very important purpose. When I close my eyes I hear the voices of the people I have encountered, their words and stories like building blocks of wisdom, just as the waves, casually over time, deposited the grains of sand that slowly formed the islands of the world.

When I hear valves, vibrating strings, and pipes all at once, an orchestra tuning up, I know the silence is coming to an end and I am ready to enter the next movement of my own personal symphony.

WATERFALL
(CHOICES, LEVELS OF LIVING)

We're all artists. Every living person has the ability. We wake every morning with a clean, white canvas before us. As the day progresses, we paint that canvas with the words we use, the gestures we make and the thoughts we think. By the end of the day, our canvas might look horribly disturbing, or it might be a masterpiece. It's all up to us. We paint our own pictures.

There are things to see in this world, things that look different early in the morning.

There's a certain happiness about some people that has nothing to do with the walls in which they live, or the car they drive.

Sometimes I feel like too many choices are tougher than no choices at all.

Oh dear Lord, did You put me here, or did I put me here? That is what I struggle with most. How do I know if You are leading me or if I'm making wrong decisions completely on my own? Well, regardless, I'm begging for help.

Start fresh daily, adding beautiful colors to your plain white canvas.

See something new out your same old window.

You own a tiny lit-up portion of it, too, of the sea. We all do. We all own a part of it, if even a glimpse.

We stopped at the bottom of a waterfall. I stood to the side and put my hands in the crashing water. Its temperature pierced through me. It was then I realized there are several levels at which we can participate in life. So, despite the group looking at me as if I were just released from a mental asylum, I quickly pulled my shoes and socks off and started to wade in the icy pool. I then chose to hold my head under the falling water. But then, I decided to go one step further and walked under the waterfall, not minding that my clothes were also getting drenched. Unfortunately, I slipped on a rock and fell like a child in the tub. I must not have looked hurt because within seconds, shoes and socks were flying everywhere and the entire group joined me. Thankfully, the path led us to a sunny spot so we could dry ourselves off and tame our goosebumps.

Today, she decided to place the important things at the top of her list. And this meant she had choices, several stages, just as a woman at the beach could choose to take her shoes off and safely walk along the shore with nothing more than her toes getting wet. She could further choose whether or not to take her clothes off and tread the chilly water waist-high. After that, she might shuffle her feet fearfully, paranoid of jellyfish or stingrays. Or, she could choose to dive under, getting her hair wet, forgetting about her makeup. Yes, a woman could choose to go only as far as the white, shallow waves washing gently against her, or she could ride the waves and risk being dashed on the mammoth spikes barricading the great ocean beyond.

Aware now of her choices, the degrees to which she could participate in daily life, she refused to bury herself in the sand of all her daily lists of things-to-do. Granted, she would not ignore responsibility or productivity, but she would transform a tedious list of errands into a life-changing map simply by adding one magnificent thing a day, something that might bring significance to her day. She promised herself she would start the New Year facing the wind like a windmill, with sturdy arms embracing the winds and generating beautiful and unlimited energy. And as the wind died down she would rest, knowing with fresh faith that it would soon start up again.

IT'S LIKE FISHING
(FINDING A PASSION)

I tried to quickly search inside myself for some form of passion, but all I saw were empty rooms and it made me feel like an old woman living alone in a mansion, yet having no furniture, or decorations to fill the space.

Every baby born to a woman is given a life. But oxygen, and the capacity to breathe, the elements of scientific living, they don't bring a person to life. Each person must decide if they want to live. We can go through life living and breathing, but this has nothing to do with truly living.

Just as one doesn't go out searching for a tarpon, we shouldn't have to go searching for a passion in life. You want to catch a tarpon and find your passion? Be still and listen.

Searching for a passion runs parallel to life. Don't make it a perpendicular search. It shouldn't interfere, and it should never become stressful. Be as confident as the fisherman who also catches the fish. Never rush it.

I feel alive and in love—in love with life.

When I looked out my window, there wasn't a view of the Gulf of Mexico, but God showed me something new out that window and I felt inspired.

LIVING IN A CASTLE (BOUNDARIES)

We build our dwellings. We can live inside a shack that is constantly threatened by this and that and always in danger of tumbling down, or we can live in a fortress.

It wasn't my jobs, where I was living, or who I was living with that continuously caused me stress in life. Rather, it was me. I was not setting boundaries and limits. Demands, requests and errands can hit you like a bulldozer, tearing down the walls that surround you. If you allow it, they will destroy your own peace of mind. Now I find myself tossing out the word 'no' as if I'm swinging a baseball bat and hitting a ball headed right for the place in which I live.

I live in a castle with walls made of boundaries, and nothing is going to tear the walls down, unless I allow it to happen.

EYES ON THE BACK OF HER HEAD (MOTHERS)

One difference between a mother and a CEO is often that mother's don't delegate. They do everything themselves.

A mother knows things. She doesn't really have eyes on the back of her head, but she has something more. She has intuition.

When life gets too busy to prepare food in a healthy manner, and to sit and slowly savor it, then life is no good. Then one needs to make emergency changes.

FIESTAS AND SIESTAS (LIGHTENING UP)

There is nothing as important as wearing the right pair of shoes. They set the mood. When my toes are warm, I'm warm and friendly. If my toes are cold, well, don't mess with me. If they're cramped, like when I wear my thin little black pointy pair, I almost always feel socially uncomfortable.

No more this, no more that! No more, no more, no more! Why is it that the words 'no more' only make us want that much more?

I love the concept of the siesta. Could the United States handle closing down business for an hour every day? Naptime would have to be mutually declared and perhaps made into law. The siesta could only work if everyone went down for a nap at the same time. Winston Churchill napped daily and claimed that when the war started, it was the only way he could cope with his responsibilities. If were president . . I would declare a war on stress and mandate every U.S. citizen to take a one-hour siesta every day—then we might have more energy for fiestas and appreciating the night.

Nourish the heart . . red wine, olive oil, romance, and careful listening.

Women hate men gawking, but if men don't gawk, we wonder why.

Thank you Lord, for answering my prayers. Thank you Lord for knowing every aspect of me down to the very number of hairs on my head. I hope you don't keep up with the number of hairs on my legs. Thank you for loving me unconditionally.

Everyone wants to believe they've bumped into an angel, and there's no reason not to believe, they decide, until they bump back into the same character a month later and he's honking and swearing one car back from them in traffic.

SAND DOLLARS (TIME GOING BY)

We spend half of life counting down to a long-awaited event, and the other half looking back.

I want to kick myself when I look back, but just as a dragonfly has four powerful wings that move independently, allowing both forward and backward flight, so too do humans have the capacity to reminisce at the same moment they're moving forward.

One day, as I walked the beach of Sanibel, I noticed the sand dollars, once buried out in the sand bars, were now arriving in the water near the shore to mate. This quietly reminded me that time was moving on.

Searching for seashells calls a person's attention to the immediate present, a therapeutic place to be.

Flowers don't need a calendar telling them when to blossom.

Time ticks by too quickly, and I feel frantic—frantic because I will never be this age again. That time had come and gone; nothing would be the same and nothing could match it, ever. I already envy my younger self.

I promise to stop and sit in parks whenever time allows. Oops! Time would NEVER allow such a thing, so I will have to MAKE time instead. And I will cook more than microwave entrees. I will use fresh basil and olive oil and no more garlic powder. I will take time to use the real thing, to peel, then mince or chop or thinly slice its cloves depending on the degree of flavor I want. And I will walk into a church and pray, or take a long walk and pray. I will do all of these things and more. I get it now why people say, "I'm going to TAKE time and go on a vacation." They never say, "Time is GIVING me a vacation." So I will do these things, not because time has become more generous, but because I will become a bit more selfish and take *a larger piece of time. No one is* GIVEN *time. It's up to people to find it, grab it, and take advantage of it in a wonderfully outlandish and selfish way.*

Life is but a passing mist and nothing lasts forever. Sadness, anger, resentment and worry pass like the clouds—some are just slower-moving storms.

Never rush life. Never rush a meal. The appetizers are as important as the dessert. The beginning is as good as the end.

There is no place I would rather be at this given time! Where am I? I'm in the moment.

No one in Spain cares about time. I wonder what they're doing in those moments of tardiness? Are they having a hard time ending incredible conversations? Savoring those last mouthfuls of paella? Engaging in a moment of poetry, passion and whatever else happens in moments of poetry and passion? Slowly sipping the last few drops of their coffee in breakable, nontransportable coffee cups? I've put too much thought into it already, but that's what I do with my moments of earliness—I think too much!

The sun rises and sets 365 times, over and over. Fridays arrive, but Mondays creep quickly around the corner every time. Time flips by like the pages of a book and I want to read it slowly, paying attention to the details. Sometimes I want to read the same sentence twice but I can't ask summer to take its time. Winter arrives when it likes, and with it shark's eyes, fighting conchs and other seashells crawling around Sanibel sandbars at low tide, attacking each other for dinner, leaving the empty shells to wash onto shore. Fall has so much to do in such little time. I will never be able to control the timing of the leaves turning orange, or crisp, or falling to the ground, or the time it takes people to rake them into piles and burn them before the snow. I can only control my own pace, and I want to walk through life, slowly, as a conductor who had once wanted the piece played only loudly, but one day interpreted it differently and decided the volume should change.

I remember there is a time for everything, but still cry at the thought of the cold, dead ground where the tulips once stood, and smile when I think of spring and the ducks arriving from the south. I close my eyes and laugh at summer and the people lining up to buy ice-cream. I go through the motions of the backward good-bye wave just thinking about fall and the ducks heading south again.

SITTING ON THE BEACH (AMBITION)

There are so many things I want to do in life and so many options that I feel overwhelmed at times. I'm afraid that I might not be able to accomplish my tablecloth scribbles. I can't even seem to find a summer job. I shouldn't feel so lost.

There are things I want to do in my life, lots of things, but what if I don't do them? What if I lose control and never accomplish any of my dreams.

We're forced to make daily choices and these choices either bring us a step closer or a step further from our goals.

There are things a woman wants in life. Things she wants from life and from herself, and they are things she must go after herself.

You might kick the bucket before reaching your goals. I might die before reaching mine. We all might. That's why the journey toward our goals, the daily steps, must mean something more.

Hop, skip, jump, run backward, or walk passionately toward your goals. Each step should add pleasure to your daily life, and if they don't, well, maybe you should reevaluate your goals to begin with.

We must enjoy the process leading up to our goals. We ought to enjoy the journey toward them as much as, and perhaps more than, the moment we reach them. More people die on the way down from the mountain than they do going up.

You are far from perfect and never will be. Measuring your perfection based on what the world claims to be perfect and is a shallow measuring device.

The world will never reward you enough for your attempted perfectionism because it will continuously demand more on a daily basis, so you may as well surrender your quest for perfection now, at this age, before you become a slave to pleasing something that will never be pleased. You will burn yourself out, leaving no time for true joy.

At this stage, my greatest present accomplishment is doing laundry.

Diaries are too good at keeping secrets. I like writing letters to God because hopefully He shares some secrets with His angels, who then might want a project to work on.

As I scribbled my dreams and goals to dear God, the results were powerful beyond belief. I felt immense peace when I surrendered my life and all the things I wanted to do over to God and His will. I am confident He reads what I write.

Surrender your dreams to God.

Every time I sit on the beach I feel entranced, invigorated with confidence, determination and inspiration to accomplish something significant in life, but what? I do not know and it's okay. When I'm at the beach, I want to live in the moment and not worry about the future. When it comes time to do something significant in life, I will know. Ideas will come to me, doors will open, and people with a purpose will pop into my life. I will be ready, but for now, for today, I just want to sit on the beach.

Christine Lemmon was born in Chicago, Illinois. When she was eight years old her family moved to Saugatuck, Michigan, where together they worked their family businesses. Her schooling was in Holland, Michigan, where she also graduated from Hope College, a private liberal arts college.

Christine lives on Sanibel Island with her husband and three children. Ideas for her books come to her while bike riding, hiking through preserves, and watching sunsets with her family.

You can visit her at:

WWW.CHRISTINELEMMON.COM